Why Don't Things Fall Up?

It was a beautiful autumn morning in the Hundred-Acre Wood. Brightly colored leaves danced on the trees as a crisp breeze sent them fluttering down, down, down.

Pooh was still asleep when—*plunk*—he fell out of bed.

"Oh, my! I was having such a sweet dream, but I guess it's time to get up and get dressed," he said.

When Pooh stepped outside, he found his welcome mat missing.

"Someone has taken my mat and left a big pile of leaves instead!" he said.

He was looking for it when—*thunk-thunk-thunk*— a shower of acorns fell from the tree and hit him on the head!

"Oh, bother!" said Pooh. "I think it's time for something sweet."

Pooh climbed a honey tree and filled his pot with honey. But as he began to climb down, his shirt got caught on a branch. "Oops!" said Pooh as he tried to tug his shirt free.

"Oh, no!" he said as the honeypot fell to the ground.

"Honeypot, here I come!" cried Pooh as he landed with a thump!

Pooh looked up to see Piglet coming
through the Hundred-Acre Wood.

"Oh, dear!" said Piglet. "Are you all
right, Pooh?"

"Yes," said Pooh. "But have you noticed
that everything is falling down around here?
Wouldn't it be nice if things could fall up
for a change?"

Pooh decided he needed to think about this some more. So he and Piglet went to his Thinking Spot to try and figure out a way to fall up.

"If only things could fall up, I wouldn't fall out of bed; I wouldn't get hit on the head with acorns; I wouldn't fall out of trees," Pooh explained as they walked.

When they got to Pooh's Thinking Spot, Pooh scratched his head and sang a little song:

> *Down, down, down!*
> *Down to the ground.*
> *Why do "up" things fall back down?*

Pooh had an idea. He tried to stand on his head. Things looked strange upside down. When Pooh saw Christopher Robin, it looked like he was floating in the sky!

"What are you doing?" asked Christopher Robin, looking down at Pooh.

"I'm trying to fall up," said Pooh. "Maybe if I'm upside down, I'll fall up instead of down."

"Oh, Pooh! You can't fall *up*!" said Christopher Robin.

Pooh leaned his head over his honeypot, opening his mouth wide.
"Now what are you doing?" asked Christopher Robin.
"I'm trying to pour the honey up into my mouth," explained Pooh.

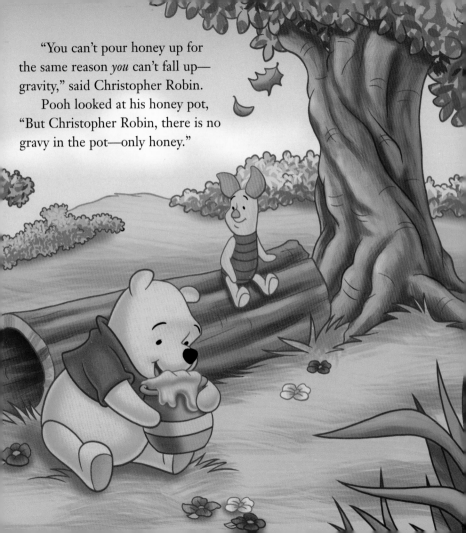

"You can't pour honey up for the same reason *you* can't fall up—gravity," said Christopher Robin.

Pooh looked at his honey pot, "But Christopher Robin, there is no gravy in the pot—only honey."

"Not gravy, *gravity*," said Christopher Robin. "It's the force that keeps everything on the ground. If there was no gravity, things would be floating all around."

"Oh, dear!" said Pooh.

"The Earth is like a giant magnet that pulls everything to it," Christopher Robin explained. "Gravity is why whatever goes up, comes down. Everything has to come down, Pooh. But not everything has to go up."

Boing-boing-boing! "Unless it bounces," said Pooh, watching Tigger bounce by.

"Yes," said Christopher Robin. "Unless it bounces—but still, it must come back down as soon as gravity starts pulling it."

Pooh, Piglet, and Christopher Robin continued their talk while walking through the Hundred-Acre Wood. Pooh was so busy looking up at all the things that fall down, he tripped on a stick and fell.

"When I fall down, it's not because I wasn't looking, it's because of gravity, right?" asked Pooh.

"Well, maybe it's a little of both!" said Christopher Robin with a smile.

Pooh had never really thought about why things fall down before.
But once Christopher Robin explained it to him, he saw gravity at
work everywhere.

At the Sandy Pit, he watched Roo practice jumping.

"Pooh, look at me!" Roo said excitedly.

Up and down, up and down, up and down...it was making Pooh dizzy!

But no matter how many times Roo went up, he always came back down.

When Pooh and Piglet walked past Owl's house, they saw a book fall from Owl's window.

"Sorry there, Rabbit," said Owl. "Would you mind throwing my book back up?"

Rabbit threw the book *up, up, up,* onto a branch above.

"Hmm," thought Pooh. "What goes up must come down—unless it gets stuck!"

As Pooh and Piglet walked away, they heard a thunk! The book had fallen to the ground. "I guess gravity even works on stuck things," said Pooh.

"Oh, bother!" exclaimed Pooh, passing by Eeyore's Gloomy Place. He looked at Eeyore's fallen house of sticks. Eeyore was trying to stack them up, but the sticks kept falling down!

"It's a much better house when the sticks stay up," said Eeyore.

"Sometimes a bit of rope and a friend can help fix a gravy—I mean, *gravity* problem," said Pooh. He and Piglet tied the sticks while Eeyore held them down.

After helping Eeyore, Pooh and Piglet walked on until they ran into Christopher Robin again.

"Hello," said Christopher Robin. "Want to watch me fly my kite?"

He ran and, with a gust of wind, the kite lifted *up, up, up*....

"Does gravity work on kites, too?" Pooh asked as the kite came crashing down.

"Yes, Pooh, it does," said Christopher Robin.

Pooh was getting tired. He and Piglet
started for home. But they didn't get very far.

"All this *up and downing* is enough to make
a fluff-and-stuff like me sleepy," said Pooh as he sat
down under his favorite tree and began to snore.

Pooh was having a sweet dream, when
something very sticky dripped down on him.

It was honey from the beehive above Pooh's head!

At this very moment, Pooh was glad that things didn't fall up.

"Mmm, gravity sure tastes good," Pooh mumbled as he drifted back to sleep.

What Goes Up, Comes Down!

No matter how high you throw the ball, it always comes down. That's because of gravity. *Gravity is the reason you walk on the ground instead of float in the sky. The world would be a very different place without gravity. There would be nothing to keep things on Earth. Can you imagine what the world would be like without gravity?*

Children learn about the world through experimenting, observing, questioning, cause and effect, and comparing. Your child can learn about gravity with these fun, simple activities.

Step 1: Throw a rubber ball up into the air several times.

Step 2: Watch what happens to the ball.

Step 3: Get a marble or small ball and a ruler and hardcover book. Lean the ruler on the book like a ramp, and place the marble at the top.

Step 4: What happens? (It rolls down. Does it roll back up by itself, or does it stay down?)

Step 5: Now put the marble at the bottom of the ramp and roll it up. Does it stay up, or roll back down? Roll the marble across a table. What happens when it reaches the edge? Does it float up or fall down?